Personalisation and

Production

Personalisation and Person-Centred Care cover, book design
and implementation by Christopher Wilson at Oberphones
Illustrations by Jo @ Kja-artists
Printed in the UK by Swallowtail Print

City & Guilds

1 Giltspur Street
London EC1A 9DD
T +44 (0)844 543 0000
learnersupport@cityandguilds.com
www.cityandguilds.com

Contents

51 **WHY?**

Introduction

The idea of this Pocket Guide is to provide a quick and easy reference guide for care staff. The book is structured around three core questions:

- ▶ **WHAT** is personalisation and person-centred care?
- ▶ **WHY** are personalised approaches so important in social care?
- ▶ **HOW** can social care workers put person-centred care into practice?

The standards of current qualifications in care have been carefully considered in writing this Pocket Guide.

Person-centred care and personalisation are key concepts in contemporary health and social care practice. Quite rightly, this is reflected in qualification standards in the sector – which require care staff to understand the meaning of these core concepts. This section therefore:

▶ **Explores the meaning of person-centred care and personalisation**

▶ **Considers the principles behind these approaches**

▶ **Reflects on the knowledge, skills and values social care workers need**

▶ **Covers the development of the personalisation agenda**

▶ **Provides a glossary of relevant terms**

▶ **Looks at some of the myths surrounding personalisation**

DEFINING PERSON-CENTRED CARE

There is a general consensus that person-centred care is user focused; promotes independence and autonomy rather than control; involves users choosing from reliable, flexible services and tends to be offered by those working with a collaborative/team philosophy.
Innes, Macpherson and McCabe 2006

Person-centred care sees service users as equal partners in planning, developing and assessing care to make sure it is most appropriate for their needs. It involves putting service users and their families at the heart of all decisions.
The Health Foundation online 2011

Person-centred care requires managers and professionals to:

- *listen to people*
- *respect their dignity and privacy*
- *recognise individual differences and specific needs including cultural and religious differences*
- *enable people to make informed choices, involving them in all decisions about their needs and care*
- *provide co-ordinated and integrated service responses*
- *involve and support carers wherever necessary.*

Department of Health 2007

DEFINING PERSONALISATION

Personalisation means thinking about care and support services in an entirely different way. This means starting with the person as an individual with strengths, preferences and aspirations and putting them at the centre of the process of identifying their needs and making choices about how and when they are supported to live their lives.

   Carr 2010

Personalisation is about enabling people to lead the lives that they choose and achieve the outcomes they want in ways that best suit them.

   Simpson 2010

Personalisation is a Government led national policy to ensure everyone who uses support should have the choice and control to shape their own lives and the services they receive.

   In Control 2011

Personalisation embodies notions of self-determination by people who use services rather than the prescriptive services approach where individuals are passive recipients of care. It empowers users to make their own choices about when, how and from whom they receive support.

Cunningham and Nickson 2010

Personalisation is about putting users at the heart of the service, enabling them to become participants in the design and delivery of the services they use.

Leadbetter 2004

PERSON-CENTRED CARE AND PERSONALISATION: MAKING THE LINKS

Person-centred approaches have a long history in care services – particularly in services for people with learning disabilities. Use of the word personalisation, however, is more recent. Many people see personalisation as a direct development from person-centred care. Effectively, contemporary social care can be seen as part of the 'era' of personalisation – which encompasses person-centred approaches whilst also considering how services can be transformed to meet the needs of individuals. In many ways, the concept of active support links very directly to person-centred approaches, and shows the links between person-centred approaches and personalisation.

DEFINING ACTIVE SUPPORT

Active support is a proven model of support that supports people ... to plan the best use of their time, with the correct level of support, to engage or participate in all activities that make up day to day living.
ARC UK 2011

Active support focuses on improving the quality of daily life ... it is focused on each individual, on what they want to do ... Active support works best when combined with person-centred planning, positive behaviour support and looking at how people communicate.
Avenues 2011

PRINCIPLES OF PERSONALISATION AND PERSON-CENTRED CARE

► The individual should be at the centre of the assessment and care planning process

► Support planning should focus on the desired outcomes for the individual and not on the convenience of the care provider

► Individuals should be recognised as experts in their own care and they should have equal input with professionals in their care planning

► Everyone is able to communicate their wishes in some way. Person-centred care recognises the individual ways in which people communicate and seeks to respond appropriately

► Where people would like others to be involved in planning their care and support (such as family members and independent advocates) this should be supported

- Person-centred care brings to life core issues such as dignity, choice and rights
- Personalised approaches focus on solutions rather than problems and strengths rather than deficits
- Risk is a part of everyone's life and individuals should be allowed to manage their own risk where appropriate
- Prevention and early intervention are fundamental to person-centred care and personalisation because they can prolong independence and quality of life
- Advice and information about finding personalised care should be available to everyone, whether or not they are eligible for local authority funding

WHAT KNOWLEDGE, SKILLS AND VALUES DO SOCIAL CARE STAFF NEED?

It is widely accepted that effective social care practice is made up of knowledge, skills and values and this is very often reflected in the qualification framework.

Effectively, a social care worker needs to develop a tool box which they can draw from – the box will contain a range of knowledge and skills which are underpinned by the values of social care.

One of the challenges of person-centred care is considering the way that care workers need to develop the required knowledge and skills. All care workers should already have the values required to be person-centred in their work. Research undertaken by **Community Care** and **Unison** (2010) identified a significant gap between the skills practitioners need and the knowledge they have. No such gaps were identified between the values social care workers have and those needed for personalised practice.

The next few pages will explore the knowledge, values and skills which social care workers will need in order to take a personalised approach in their practice.

Health and social care workers need knowledge of:

▶ Legal and policy framework
▶ Policy and procedure in relation to direct payments and personalised support planning
▶ Theories which support personalisation
▶ Systems and how to navigate them
▶ Research around personalised approaches
▶ Models of self-directed support
▶ Barriers and enablers
▶ Best practice

Health and social care workers need skills in:

► Communication and relationship building
► Partnership working (co-production)
► Empowerment
► Creativity (an ability to think 'outside the box')
► Facilitating
► Evaluation
► Advocacy
► Navigation

VALUES

Social care has a long tradition of having a clear professional value base. Many writers believe that person-centred care and personalisation have developed out of this value base.

For example, **Carr** (2008) believes that personalisation has grown out of the core social care values of:

- *Human rights*
- *Personal dignity*
- *Self-determination*
- *Good person-centred practice*

Lelkes (2010) states that in order to implement personalisation, social care workers need to build on the core values of:

- *Putting people first*
- *Respect for individuals and self-determination*
- *Listening and empowering*
- *Recognising and addressing potential conflict*
- *Safeguarding needs and the capacity of individuals*
- *Being sensitive to diversity and putting people in control*

THE DIMENSIONAL APPROACH

Duffy and Fulton (2010) provide a useful model for understanding personalisation. They see four outer dimensions and one inner dimension to the concept, as illustrated in the figure below:

The outer dimensions, which both feed into and feed out of the central dimension of personal resilience, are described as follows:

Capacities: Personalisation and person-centred care should provide people with the ability to exercise and develop their own personal capacities, strengths and gifts. This will involve supporting people to express their dreams, wishes, hopes and aspirations. It is also important to support people to build on their capacities by ensuring that people recognise where they have solved a difficulty before. When people recognise that they have overcome difficulties in the past it can strengthen their resolve and ensure they feel more able to cope with fututre difficulties.

Connections: Personalised approaches enable people to develop relationships with others in order to thrive and develop. People need to find ways to make connections across a range of relationships. Many models of personal resilience refer to the importance of people making connections with others in similar circumstances as well as the need for strong personal networks.

Access: Person-centred care means that people are provided with access to the wider community in which they live. They need to share in general services and meet people in open and inclusive environments. This has long been an expressed aim in social care but there is still a long way to go in terms of inclusive experiences for service users.

Control: Personalisation and person-centred care provides people with the control to shape their own lives. Without control people become increasingly vulnerable, subject to power and control by others. People need to feel that others recognise them as the expert on their own life and that they have the power to control their experiences.

BUILDING BLOCKS FRAMEWORK

Towell (2008) proposes a framework of three building blocks which demonstrates the way in which personalised support is a key aspect of citizenship:

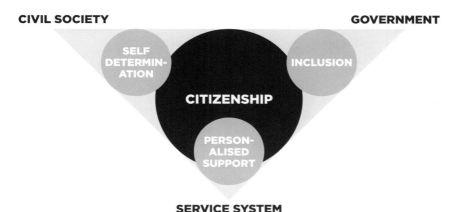

Towell (2008) goes on to show the way in which these building blocks provide a framework around which to array the key elements in national strategies for change:

THE SEVEN Ps

The Department of Health (2010) refer to the seven P principles which provide the basis for their vision of modern social care:

With six of the Ps surrounding and supporting the personalisation agenda, they illustrate the changes that will need to be made to truly implement personalised approaches, developing on from the ideals of person-centred care.

Partnership: There is a need for better 'joined-up working' between families, communities, health, social care and support services.

Prevention: There should be a renewed emphasis on keeping people as independent as possible for as long as they feel able.

Plurality: There should be increased diversity in service provision.

Protection: People should not have to worry about becoming more vulnerable; support is there when they need it to ensure people will be safe and secure.

Productivity: Increased local accountability should drive innovations to increase productivity and quality.

People: The whole workforce will need to work alongside service users and their carers to lead the transformation of social care.

THE DEVELOPMENT OF PERSON-CENTRED CARE

The beginnings of person-centred approaches can be traced back to the work of **Carl Rogers** (1958) and the way that he developed what he termed client-centred therapy. Ideas around person-centred practice then developed in America and moved across to the UK. At first, the ideas influenced learning disability services, although the **Joseph Rowntree Foundation** (2006) recognises that person-centred approaches have now 'spread from learning disability services to influence the whole of adult social care.'

Tom Kitwood, who founded the Bradford dementia group, developed the initial ideas of person-centred care into work with people with dementia. From this point, person-centred approaches became more influential across the whole of adult care. As the idea of person-centred practice became more widespread it impacted on Government policy and legislation and further developed into the concept of personalisation and, more recently, self-directed support.

THE DEVELOPMENT OF PERSONALISATION

It is important for care staff to understand the development of person-centred care and how this has progressed with the current legal and policy framework supporting personalisation.

As early as 1990, the **NHS and Community Care Act*** referred to the importance of a 'needs led approach' and 'individually tailored packages of care'. There was also an emphasis on providing care for people in their own homes, rather than in institutions. The Act also laid a duty on local authorities to assess people for social care and support so that they could get the care that they needed. This followed on from the 'care in the community' policy of the 1980s, which emptied out the traditional care homes, but often made little real provision for the people who had to leave.

* The NHS and Community Care Act applies to England, Scotland and Wales only.
  It is not on the statute book in Northern Ireland save for sections 59, 61 and 62.

After years of campaigning by disability rights groups, the **Community Care (Direct Payments) Act** (1996)* passed into law. It marked a new direction in social care because people were able to take cash payments to buy the care of their choice. At first the Act applied only to people under 65 who had a physical or learning disability, but in the following years it was extended to include; people with mental health problems, older people, carers and parents of disabled children. The majority of people chose to stay with the services provided for them by their local authority, but many of those who took direct payments experienced a much improved quality of life. Instead of being told what services they would receive, they had control of their own care.

* Social Work (Scotland) Act (1968). As amended 1999.
   Northern Ireland Act (1974). As amended 1999.

The Valuing People White Paper (2001) stated the aim of making direct payments available to more people with a learning disability and emphasised the need for 'person-centred planning' in social care.

The same year the **National Service Framework for Older People** set new standards with the aim of improving the quality of health and social care for older people. One of the main themes of the framework was 'respecting people', and providing person-centred care.

The **Health and Social Care Act** (2001)* demonstrated Government commitment to direct payments and subsequent Government guidance placed a mandatory duty on local authorities to offer direct payments to people eligible for services.

* Sections 63–65 and 70 only relevant to Northern Ireland.

Improving the Life Chances of Disabled People (2005) introduced the idea of individual budgets for disabled people. Individual budgets differed from personal budgets in that they were made up of a number of different funding streams, whereas personal budgets are funded from social care money. Individual budgets generally proved too complex to manage because of the difficulties of combining funding streams from different departments.

Independence, Wellbeing and Choice (2005), an England-only Department of Health Green Paper, recognised the important role that social care services can play in improving people's lives by ensuring that they had much greater control over their own support. It also laid out the skills that the social care workforce of the future would need to develop to meet the challenges of the changing model of social care delivery.

Our Health, Our Care, Our Say – a new direction for community service
(Department of Health White Paper, 2006) looked forward to:

high quality support meeting people's aspirations for independence and greater control over their lives, making services flexible and responsive to individual needs. We will build on what we have done, putting people more in control and shifting to a greater emphasis on prevention.

Putting People First: A Shared Vision and Commitment to Transformation of Adult Social Care (2007) proposed that people should have their own individual/personal budgets, that the money should be used to achieve the outcomes they desired and that they should be able to plan and control their own support.

THINK LOCAL, ACT PERSONAL

Changes to the Government of England have led to debates about whether the personalisation agenda will continue to be implemented. However, it is widely agreed that 'The main political parties are now settled on the language of empowerment, the creation of 'user-led services' and on personalisation.'
Griffiths 2009

Think Local, Act Personal is an agreement between over 30 key health and social care organisations from national and local Government, the private sector and the voluntary sector. It was launched in January 2011 and confirmed the Conservative and Liberal Democrat Coalition's commitment to personalisation. The agreement recognises the important role that **Putting People First** played in the drive towards personalisation, but also draws on the lessons learnt from its implementation and 'focuses on areas where further action is required'.

There is an emphasis on closer working between health and social care, developing efficient local social care markets, prevention and early intervention and more local community involvement. Improvement will be sector-led rather than government-led.

The principles of personalisation remain at the centre of this change, underpinning a leaner, more outcome focussed and outward facing role for the public sector. The overall aim is to secure a shift to a position where as many people as possible are enabled to stay healthy and actively involved in their communities for longer and delaying or avoiding the need for targeted services. Those however who do need such help, including many people at the end of life, should have maximum control over this, with the information, means (financial and practical) and confidence to make it a reality.

Think Local, Act Personal Partnership 2011

DIVERSITY ACROSS THE UK

In terms of health and social care, the last decade or so has seen increasing diversity in law and policy across the four nations as more powers have been devolved from Westminster to the individual nations.

Whilst the legislation and national policy directives do differ, political commitment to personalisation as the way forward for social care provision is consistent across the four nations. For example, the Northern Ireland Department of Health, Social Services and Public Safety has declared a commitment to promoting self-directed care and personalisation (Gray and Horgan 2010), whilst the Scottish Government has recognised that:

Personalisation is the foundation of good social care practice and is already the goal of social care in Scotland.
Changing Lives Service Development Group 2008

GLOSSARY OF PERSONALISATION TERMS

Advocacy

The role of the advocate is to represent the interests of the service user. This involves supporting service users to make their own decisions about their care, ensuring that the care they receive is of a high standard and, quite frequently, enabling people to challenge decisions made by local authorities or other organisations.

Brokerage

The role of a broker is to provide advice and information, based on a good knowledge of local service provision, to service users to enable them to choose a care package tailored to their needs. The broker may also help with support planning. Professional brokers are paid for the service they provide.

Co-production

Service users (and their carers and families) know what makes a good service and have the skills and expertise to help make service improvements. Co-production is the process by which services recognise this experience and involve service users as equal partners in service design and delivery. The co-production process can also be used in commissioning services.

Direct payments

Direct payments are available to people who have been assessed as eligible for free social care by their local authority. The payments are given to the individual (or someone acting on their behalf) so that they can arrange and buy their own care rather than use services provided by the local authority. Personal budgets may be taken as a direct payment.

Indicative budget

Following an initial assessment of needs, service users will be allocated an indicative budget so that they know how much they can spend on their care and support. Once they have demonstrated how they will spend their budget through the process of support planning and the local authority has agreed with their plan, the indicative budget will be confirmed as the personal budget.

Market shaping (also known as building provider capacity)

The aim of market shaping is to build the capacity of the local social care provider market. By actively encouraging the development of the market within their local communities, local authorities can improve the range of provision for service users.

Navigation

In the context of personalisation, navigation is a skill that is becoming increasingly important to social workers. It is about knowing how to find your way through what may be a complex landscape of local care provision care so that you can arrive at the best possible care package for each individual. Supporting service users to find their own way around the system is also an important aspect of a navigation role.

Personal budget

A regular payment, based on personal need, to service users to cover the cost of their care and support. Personal budgets may be paid directly to the service user, managed by someone else on their behalf, by a trust or by a social services department.

Prevention

The aim of prevention services is to support people by offering advice and help to enable them to remain independent for longer. By recognising possible risk factors in people's lives (eg social isolation or poor health because of an inadequate diet or lack of exercise) and intervening at an early stage people can be helped to have a better quality of life.

Reablement

Support given to someone (usually, but not always, an older person) to help them regain daily skills that may have been lost because of poor physical or mental health. Reablement support is provided for a limited period, usually 6–12 weeks, and the focus is on helping people to do things for themselves so that they can manage on their own.

Resource Allocation System (RAS)

The method by which local authorities assess the amount of money an individual will need to pay for their social care and support.

Risk Enablement Panel

If agreement cannot be reached about the level of risk that is acceptable in a support plan, a Risk Enablement Panel will meet to discuss the situation. These panels only meet when there is a case to be considered and are the responsibility of local authority adult safeguarding teams. They are generally made up of the service user and supporter/s, people working in adult social care and other agencies, and any carers who may be particularly affected by the decision.

Self-directed support/planning

This is the philosophy of putting the person at the centre of the support and planning process so that they have choice and control and their care is designed to meet their individual needs. This term is used by **In Control** instead of personalisation.

Signposting

Signposting means to point people in the direction of information that they should find useful. For example, local authorities have social care pages on their websites that provide links to documents and other websites that will be of interest to people who want to know more about social care.

Support planning

The process of planning care and support. This involves defining the outcomes desired by the service user and showing how the money allocated in the indicative budget will be used to ensure that these outcomes can be achieved.

MYTHS AND REALITIES

Myth	Reality
Personalisation is only for people who are eligible for local authority funding	Personalisation is for everyone who needs care. Self-funders are equally entitled to expect personalised care
Personalisation is only for people who are cared for in their own homes	People in residential care should have the same expectation of personalised care as those who are cared for in their own homes
Personalisation means that we won't be professional care workers in the future	Professional care workers have a vital role to play in personalised services. Local authorities will remain responsible for the care and safety of service users and will depend on the expertise of trained professionals to do this work

Myth	Reality
The real motivation behind personalisation is that the government wants to save money on social care	The recognition of people having a basic right to self-determination is probably the most significant motivation behind personalisation. There was a strong movement from disability rights groups and others towards personalisation because they wanted more choice and control over their lives. Also, personalised care is not necessarily cheaper than traditional care
Care providers are not in favour of personalisation because they think it will be bad for their businesses	Many care providers are enthusiastic about personalisation and are tailoring their services to meet the needs of their customers

JOINING UP THE PIECES ...

Person-centred care and personalisation are all about the uniqueness of individuals and making connections. These approaches require joined-up thinking. The pieces of the jigsaw need to be put together to fully understand the nature of personalisation and person-centred care:

WHY are personalised approaches so important in social care ?

In order to practise effectively, social care workers need to understand why person-centred care and personalisation are so central to contemporary social care practice. This section therefore:

▶ **Considers why personalised approaches are so important**
▶ **Explores the outcomes of personalised approaches for service users and carers**
▶ **Covers the traditional models of service delivery which personalisation seek to 'transform'**

WHY ARE PERSONALISED APPROACHES SO IMPORTANT IN SOCIAL CARE?

▶ Every service user is unique, with differing circumstances and needs. It follows that their needs can only be met by support which focuses on them as an individual

▶ Everyone has a unique history and 'life story'. This will impact on their needs, their life choices and their behaviour. Support and care will only be effective if it takes the unique life history into account

▶ Traditional models of service delivery create climates where power is easily abused and where service users are disempowered. This increases both dependence and vulnerability

▶ Person-centred care and personalised approaches have very positive outcomes for service users. For example, people report improvements in general health and wellbeing

- Everyone wants to have control over their own life and has the right to make choices – only person-centred approaches to care promote choice and control
- The population of the UK is becoming increasingly diverse. Personalisation leads to services which are more culturally sensitive and person-centred care promotes culturally competent practice in care staff
- People have a legal right to make choices and to access care which promotes dignity and respect. Quite rightly, people are making more demands on services to provide more person-centred care
- The number of unpaid carers (mostly family and friends of service users) in the UK is growing rapidly. Carers report increased satisfaction with person-centred care and they are more likely to accept support services which work on a personalised basis

CHANGING DEMOGRAPHICS

The global population is changing. People are living longer and improved health care has led to people having more complex needs. This has presented major challenges to governments around the world. **Kerr and Reid** (2008) point out that personalisation is a direct result of these changes. They see it as the:

Government response to the dilemmas of how to pay for the future social care system – especially as the population ages, people are living longer with more complex needs and there are fewer working tax payers – and at the same time, provide for the rising expectations of people to higher quality and more individually responsive services.

In addition to the ageing population, the UK has become more culturally diverse. Whilst at the time of writing, the results of the most recent census are not available, it is estimated that in England around 10% of the population is from a minority ethnic group (**Office for National Statistics** 2010). In some parts of the UK this figure is much higher (for example, in London just under 40% of the population is described by the Office of National Statistics as non-white. In Wales this figure is 7%).

This diversity adds real strength to our population and should be valued and celebrated. It also means that the needs of the population and the outcomes that people desire are becoming more and more diverse as the population changes. As a result person-centred care and personalised approaches to service delivery are all the more vital.

WHAT IS THE IMPACT FOR SERVICE USERS?

Research indicates high satisfaction levels for service users who receive personalised support. For example, **Edwards and Waters** (2008) report that in their research:

> *55% of people stated that they spent more time with people they wanted to be with*
>
> *77% reported improvements in quality of life*
>
> *63% reported that they took more part in their local communities*
>
> *47% reported improvements in general health and wellbeing*
>
> *72% reported that they had more choice and control in their lives*
>
> *59% reported that they had more personal dignity*

Ben

*I have mental health problems and am not able to work at the moment.
Since I have had a personal budget the quality of my life has really improved.
A friend of mine, Jane, comes every week to help me do my grocery shop.
She does not want to be paid, but she has to take the bus to my house and
now I can pay for her fares. My physical health was deteriorating because for
quite a long time I found it difficult to go out. It was agreed by my local
authority that I could be funded to take out a gym membership. I now go to the
local gym at least three times a week and feel much fitter and healthier.*

WHAT IS THE IMPACT FOR CARERS?

Friends and family members acting as unpaid carers are sometimes reluctant to seek support and accept formal care for their 'loved one'. This can lead to significant difficulties for carers and service users, possibly increasing the vulnerability of service users and placing carers under increasing pressure. Certainly where informal carers are involved there can be situations where services become involved at a significantly later stage. Where services are tailored to individual needs, carers may be more likely to accept a level of support at an earlier stage which can prolong the informal caring arrangement.

Alzheimer Scotland (2011) states that, when empowered to direct their own services:

families effectively combine state resources around their own natural supports – creating truly personalised support.

Lorna

My husband Tim has early onset dementia. I left my job so that I could look after him, but soon found that I was spending nearly every minute of my day caring for him and I could not do anything else. Tim was assessed for his care needs by the local authority. It was decided that he was eligible for a personal budget that I manage on his behalf. I spend it on regular help around the house and garden, which means that I can focus on caring for Tim and I am under far less stress. Tim's personal budget also pays for occasional respite care so that I can have some time to myself to recharge my batteries.

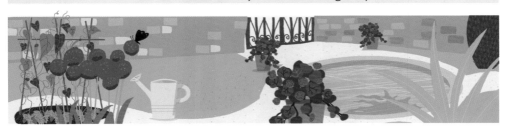

'ONE SIZE FITS ALL ...'

Traditionally social care services have operated according to a 'one size fits all' model. Services were not tailored to the needs of the individual. People had no choice other than to accept or decline the services that were provided or commissioned by their local authority.

TAILOR-MADE APPROACHES

Person-centred care directly challenges the 'one size fits all' model by recognising that people are unique and require 'tailor-made' approaches which meet their individual needs. Personalisation takes the challenge further still by recognising that service users need to have choices and the control to design services which will meet their unique needs.

Although personalisation is closely associated with personal budgets, it is about more than simply enabling people to have financial control over their own care. It is about ensuring that people have choice and control over their own lives.

THE 'GIFT MODEL'

Traditional methods of care have been referred to as the gift model. Based on the tragedy and charity models of disability, the gift model is about tasks being carried out for people. Active support on the other hand is about working with people to enable them to take part in all the activities of daily life.

The provision of care as a 'gift' negates rights to choice and control – after all, gifts are given without the recipient having a choice. There is a societal expectation that people are 'grateful' for gifts and have no right to make demands.

Challenging the gift model of care is widely supported by European policy makers, who recognise that:

> *The disability movement challenged the term 'care' replacing it with 'the right to support'. For many disabled activists, the very concept of 'care' embodies an oppressive history in which the practices of paid (particularly professional) and unpaid carers have maintained disabled and older people in a position of unwanted dependency, at worst abused, segregated and stripped of their dignity, at best patronised and protected from exercising any agency over their lives. Instead care needs are reinterpreted as having choice and control as the strategies for the empowerment of disabled people.*
> **Social Platform** 2010:1

THE 'HOTEL MODEL'

This term is often used to refer to what might also be called institutionalised care or 'batch' living. In hotels, everything is done for the 'guest' – staff carry out all the domestic duties and guests do not get the opportunity to engage in activities which contribute to the running of the 'hotel'.

'Hotel' model services are institutionalised services which are organised largely around staff needs rather than those of the individuals they support (for example, with inflexible meal times, bed times, etc), and they provide a poor quality of life for service users.

Writers such as **Gardner** (2011) describe personalisation as a way of both 'thinking' and 'doing'. This section therefore considers how social care workers can put person-centred work and personalisation into by practice by exploring:

▶ **Theories and approaches that support person-centred work**

▶ **Practical guidelines for being person-centred**

▶ **Person-centred thinking tools**

▶ **Person-centred approaches to risk**

In some ways, the most straightforward way to answer the question *how does a social care worker put person-centred approaches and personalisation into practice?* is to revisit the **WHAT?** section of this book and simply do that! However, it's often easier to say than do – so the next few pages will explore how to put some of the essential aspects of person-centred care into practice.

▶ **Keeping things user-centred**
▶ **Promoting dignity and respect**
▶ **Developing empathy**
▶ **Promoting individuality**

KEEPING THINGS USER-CENTRED

One of the key principles of personalisation is putting people at the 'heart' of the service, and maintaining the central focus on the individual.

Sometimes with the demands of contemporary care work, health and social care workers can lose sight of this. The focus instead might be on management systems, demands from other professionals, resource constraints and carer perspectives (to name just a few). It might seem obvious – but the most important aspect of person-centred care is remembering just why you are there – for the service user!

DIGNITY AND RESPECT

Perhaps one of the most important ways that we can work in a person-centred way is to ensure that we treat people with dignity and respect. Having developed the ideas of person-centred care in dementia services, Tom Kitwood coined the term 'personhood' which he defined as:

A standing or status that is bestowed upon one human being, by others in the context of relationship and social being. It implies recognition, respect and trust.
Kitwood 1997

Recognising the vital importance of dignity in social care, the Government launched a Dignity in Care Campaign in November 2006. This aims to put 'dignity and respect at the heart of care services'. Part of the campaign is a ten point dignity challenge.

THE TEN POINT DIGNITY CHALLENGE

1 Have a zero tolerance of all forms of abuse

2 Support people with the same respect you would want for yourself or a member of your family

3 Treat each person as an individual by offering a personalised service

4 Enable people to maintain the maximum possible level of independence, choice and control

5 Listen and support people to express their needs and wants

6 Respect people's right to privacy

7 Ensure people feel able to complain without fear of retribution

8 Engage with family members and carers as care partners

9 Assist people to maintain confidence and a positive self-esteem

10 Act to alleviate people's loneliness and isolation

The Social Care Institute for Excellence (2010) **states that research indicates that eight main factors promote dignity in care:**

► **Choice and control**: enabling people to make their own choices
► **Communication**: speaking to people with respect and listening to them effectively ('When new staff start, they always say what their name is and ask me what I like to be called. It's a small thing but I appreciate it.')
► **Eating and nutritional care**: providing nutritional meals that meet people's needs and choices and providing support where needed ('Mealtimes aren't just about the food we eat. It's about who you eat with, where you sit, is it comfortable?')
► **Pain management**: ensuring people have the help and medication they need to improve their quality of life.

- **Personal hygiene**: enabling people to maintain their usual standards of personal hygiene. ('Care is a very intimate thing. The closer the person is to someone that you like and respect, or have interests in common with the better.')
- **Practical assistance**: enabling people to maintain their independence through the provision of appropriate levels of support and assistance
- **Privacy**: respecting peoples' privacy and personal space
- **Social inclusion**: supporting people to keep in contact with their family and friends and to participate in the social activities they choose ('Her son had told us that music had been a very important part of her life. So we would sing a hymn to her and she started again picking up those tunes. It's given her back some of her dignity.')

DIGNITY WHEN PROVIDING ASSISTANCE WITH EATING AND DRINKING

▶ Discuss the menu with the person you are assisting, in order to establish their preferences

▶ Ask about how much salt/sauce, etc, a person requires, never assume

▶ Establish and respect any religious/cultural needs in relation to diet. Never assume dietary preferences on the basis of culture. Information from relatives may be needed if a person cannot express any such needs themselves, for example, due to mental health difficulties

▶ If you are helping a person to shop or preparing meals for them, comply with their requests, even if they may not be the choices that you would make

▶ Recognise that time requirements will vary between individuals and for the same individual at different times. For example, a person with multiple sclerosis may be far more independent one day than the previous day, or in the morning than the afternoon

- Do not expect people to eat cold food. It may therefore be necessary to consider means of keeping food warm, if it takes them a long time to eat (eg a covered dish)
- Promptly clean up any spills on a person's clothing, skin, etc
- Do not 'mash' or mix food together, unless a specialist assessment indicates this is necessary. Provide food items separately, as you would eat yourself
- Make food look appetising
- Focus on your role and task – where an individual needs physical support to eat and drink it is vital that the care worker offering support focuses on that individual and their needs rather than talking to another worker, looking around the room, etc
- Do not talk to people when they have their mouth full
- Refer people for specialist assessment if this is necessary – for example, speech and language therapists can make a specialist assessment and offer support where people have swallowing difficulties, occupational therapists can offer advice and assistance with specialist equipment, etc

DIGNITY WHEN PROVIDING ASSISTANCE WITH PERSONAL CARE

▶ Always explain what care duty you wish to undertake and ask permission

▶ Establish with the person precisely what help they require – for example, an individual may want help in washing their feet, but be able to manage other parts of their body independently

▶ If a person is confused, it may be necessary to explain many times what you are doing and why. This needs to be done sensitively. If a person has short term memory problems, then finding someone undressing/washing them when they cannot remember why, is traumatic

▶ Even if you are in a noisy environment, attempt to keep explanations discreet, lean closer to the person you are helping rather than raise your voice

▶ Always ensure doors are closed, and prevent intrusions when a person is bathing/undressing, etc, including those by other staff members (there may be exceptions to this in emergency situations)

- ▶ If it is necessary for another person to become involved, eg additional assistance in getting a person out of the bath, explain why and ask permission
- ▶ Within a hospital ward setting, remain aware of flimsy bed curtains!
- ▶ Establish any cultural requirements in relation to washing
- ▶ Encourage and respect personal choice within care processes, eg: ensure choices of clothing, soap, toiletries, etc
- ▶ Respect the lifestyle choices that people make when assisting with personal care – for example, respecting people's choice of hairstyle, clothing, etc
- ▶ Remain focused on the individual – for example, if you are working with another member of staff do not converse with them when providing personal care to the individual

DIGNITY WHEN PROVIDING SUPPORT WITH CONTINENCE MANAGEMENT

▶ Recognise that continence is an environmental as well as medical issue. For example, a person may be able to confidently reach the toilet within his or her own home, but not within a care environment

▶ Try and ensure that a person has appropriate access to toilets, taking into account mobility/orientation issues, etc

▶ When attending to or inquiring about continence needs, always be discreet, for example, in drawing curtains around beds, ensuring toilet doors are shut

▶ Remove used continence aids promptly, discreetly and safely

▶ Avoid leaving continence aids belonging to an individual, on public display

- Be familiar with personal continence routines and capacity levels for continence aids – for example, if and when a person needs to be reminded to go to the toilet, etc. This may be particularly relevant for people with short-term memory difficulties
- Do not make jokes about the support being provided
- Use language which is appropriate for adults rather than children – for example, do not refer to continence wear as nappies

EMPATHY

Empathy really refers to trying to put yourself in someone else's shoes and imagining how the situation feels for them. It is seen as an essential skill for social care workers and is recognised as vital in practices such as 'dementia care mapping' (DCM) which Kitwood describes as:

> *a serious attempt to take the standpoint of the person with dementia, using a combination of empathy and observational skill.*
> **Kitwood** 1997

Person-centred work relies on the development of what is referred to as 'empathic relationships' – **Janet Tolan** (2003) describes this as a relationship where the worker is able to 'see the whole world as the other person sees it and is wholly accepting of that world'. She goes on to say that there is no formula for empathy and no magic or easy route to getting it right. However, the starting point is actively listening to the individual – not only through traditional listening to words but also by using your observational skills. The following poem written by a person with learning disabilities illustrates the importance of active listening:

To work with me,
You have to listen to me
And you can't just listen with our ears.
Because it will go to our head to fast. You have to listen with our whole body.

If you listen slow, some of what I say
Will enter our heart

Written by a **Canadian student with learning disabilities**
source unknown

RESPONDING TO INDIVIDUALITY

Whilst a very few social care workers will work with just one service user (usually in a PA role) the majority of social care workers will work with a large number of service users.

The different people you work with may, in some ways, have much in common. However, they will also be unique in many ways. As human beings, we all share a common humanity and in some ways we are all the same (for example, biologically). In *some* ways, *some* people are the same – for example, we may share common characteristics with others (such as whether we are a man or a woman). Finally though, in other ways we are all different and therefore unique.

The figure opposite taken from **Thompson** (1994) demonstrates this well:

IN SOME
WAYS WE
ARE ALL
UNIQUE

SOME PEOPLE ARE THE SAME
IN SOME WAYS (EG GENDER)

IN SOME WAYS WE ARE ALL THE SAME (EG BIOLOGY)

Traditional services tend to focus on the lower areas of the pyramid – the ways in which people are the same, because these areas are easier to 'cater for' in service delivery. However, social care staff must focus on the ways in which we are all different.

Whenever a social care worker (often proudly) says 'I treat everyone the same', we should be immediately alert to the fact that they are not working in a person-centred way. In fact, we should treat everyone 'uniquely'. A key aspect to person-centred practice is focusing on what makes people *different* rather than what makes us the same.

One of the purposes of assessment is to identify what makes each of us a unique individual. Care provided to people *must* focus on this uniqueness and respond to the individuality of each service user.

Recognising what makes each of us individual is vital for social care staff. The list of what makes us unique is endless, but some of the key points include:

- Our name – and how we like it to be used
- Our life 'story'
- Our family – and how we relate to them
- Our friends
- What we like
- What we don't like
- Our accent
- Our sexuality
- The way we dress
- Our body language
- Our habits

WHAT ELSE MIGHT MAKE US UNIQUE?

- ▶ The way we feel about things
- ▶ Our religion
- ▶ Our culture
- ▶ What we dream about
- ▶ What we want from life
- ▶ What makes us happy
- ▶ What makes us sad
- ▶ What relationships we have
- ▶ Our hobbies
- ▶ What makes a good day for us

HOW MUCH OF THIS COULD YOU SAY ABOUT THE PEOPLE YOU WORK WITH?

BIOGRAPHICAL APPROACH

Sometimes referred to as a narrative approach, the biographical approach to social care is essentially about taking the person's life story into account when working with them. As a theory it is fundamentally simple – think about how often we read the 'autobiography' of a celebrity to understand 'where they are coming from' – or how interested people seem to be in the lives of celebrities (through magazines and papers etc.). When we meet someone new we often ask them about their lives, it shows interest and respect and gives something to base conversation on. The biographical approach recognises this – it reflects the influence of a person's life story on them and is a key part of person-centred care.

Many social care workers use a biographical approach – often without recognising it. When I want to illustrate the importance of the biographical approach and the way that it promotes person-centred working, I am reminded about a situation where I observed a review meeting about an older man with dementia. He had recently been admitted to a hospital ward and his behaviour had become increasingly difficult for the service to manage. He was moving furniture around the service – initially blocking the door to his room, then posing health and safety risks by moving furniture and equipment around in shared environments. The multi-disciplinary review meeting was called to plan an appropriate response to the situation.

The consultant went first, saying he felt that the man was agitated because of his dementia and that medication might help. The psychologist said he felt that the man was trying to communicate his need for privacy. The occupational therapist said that he felt if the man could be engaged in more appropriate activities during the day he would not feel the need to move things around, whilst the specialist nurse talked about the specific stages of dementia and how she felt this may be relevant. The social care worker (very quietly and lacking in confidence) said that she had spoken to the man and his family about his life and she discovered that the family ran a business, initially set up by the man. It was a removals firm. She wondered if this might be having an impact on his behaviour.

This clearly illustrates the value of taking a person-centred approach which recognises the impact of a person's life story. Others had focused on their professional perspectives – whilst the social care worker had placed herself in the shoes of the service user and recognised the fact that every time he had been somewhere new in his life – he was there to move the furniture. Sometimes a biographical approach (essentially a simple understanding) can provide the most helpful perspective.

This 'story' illustrates the importance of taking a biographical approach to working with service users and the fact that it is essential to know about a person's life history to work with them.

Social care workers need to find out about a person's life story, and sometimes this involves detective work. How you do this will differ, depending on what the person can tell you about themselves.

The various methods that social care workers use in finding about a service user's life history include:

- Talking to the service user themselves
- Actively listening to everything the service user says (not just what they say verbally!)
- Asking family members about the person's life
- Looking through photographs with the person
- Reading past records and reports
- Using a 'life story book' (sometimes prepared by family members or by staff who know the person well)
- Using reminiscence group work
- Playing music, films, etc, that would have been popular when the person was younger – and watching the individual for responses

What do you know about the life stories of the people you work with? How did you find that out?

STRENGTHS PERSPECTIVE

The strengths perspective is not a theory in itself. It has been developing for many years (arguably 40 years or more) and has become a key part of person-centred thinking. The strengths perspective recognises that in the past, assessments and care have focused largely on people's needs and deficits rather than on their strengths, abilities and resilience.

Adopting a person-centred approach means adopting the strengths perspective. **Saleebey** (1996) generated the following comparison of what he termed 'professional pathologising' (which he saw in many traditional models – particularly the medical model) against the strengths perspective:

Pathology	Strengths
Person is defined as a 'case'; symptoms add up to a diagnosis	Person is defined as unique; traits, talents, resources add up to strengths

Pathology	Strengths
Service user accounts are filtered by a professional to aid the generation of a diagnosis	Personal accounts are the essential route to knowing and appreciating the person
Professional devises treatment or care plan	Service user is fully involved in the care plan decisions
Professional is the expert about service user's life	The individual and their family are the experts
Possibilities for choice, control, commitment and development limited by label/diagnosis or condition	Possibilities for choice, control, commitment and personal development are open
Professional's knowledge, skills and connections are principal resources for service user	The strength, capacities and adaptive skills of the individual, family or community are the principal resources
Support centred on reducing the effects of symptoms and the negative effects of emotions or relationships	Support focused on getting on with life, affirming and developing values and commitments

POWER AND EMPOWERMENT

Power and empowerment are central components of person-centred approaches and personalisation. For example, **Parley** (2001) states that person-centred approaches are about deliberately shifting the power towards service users. **Sanderson** (2003) states that person-centred approaches require a change in thinking about power relations, claiming that care staff and services need to operate from a position where they have power with service users rather than power over service users.

Whilst empowerment is a word often used in health and social care, it is widely misunderstood. One of the basic principles of empowerment is the recognition that it is not an easy thing to do.

It is important for social care workers to revisit the basics of empowerment and understand it more clearly. The basics of empowering practice are summarised by **Maclean and Harrison** (2011) as:

▶ Recognising power differentials
▶ Listening and hearing
▶ Acknowledging the dignity of risk
▶ Seeing people as experts on their own situation and on the services they receive
▶ Taking a solution-focused approach
▶ Facilitating user involvement
▶ Encouraging hopefulness
▶ Developing positive attitudes and practice
▶ Helping service users to develop resources
▶ Encouraging support networks

USE OF LANGUAGE

Often referred to negatively as 'political correctness', the importance of language in the personalisation agenda cannot be underestimated. Language is all about power and one direct application of empowerment is about an appropriate use of language.

Language creates barriers between people, it can dehumanise and ultimately depersonalise.

Depersonalisation: 'ic' is often added to a diagnosis to describe someone – diabetic, schizophrenic, etc. This is incredibly depersonalising. It is much more appropriate to refer to someone as living with a diagnosis of diabetes rather than as 'a diabetic'.

Dehumanisation: the process of dehumanisation is about people not being seen as a valued human being or the worth of a person being reduced so that they are seen as not quite human (sub-human). Language in social care is very often dehumanising. Perhaps the best example of this is the language used around personal care. For example, people generally 'eat' but as soon as someone comes into contact with social care services they will be referred to as 'feeding themselves' or needing to be 'fed'. In other situations we only refer to feeding about babies and animals. The central message received by people is that they are now less than human.

POSITIVE PERSON WORK (KITWOOD)

Kitwood developed the concept of positive person work, which is essentially about good quality communication, involving:

- Warmth
- Holding
- Celebration
- Acknowledgement
- Genuineness
- Empowerment
- Enabling
- Including

- Belonging
- Fun
- Relaxed pace
- Respect
- Acceptance
- Facilitation
- Collaboration
- Recognition

THE VIPS APPROACH

Dawn Brooker has developed an equation to illustrate what she sees as the four elements of person-centred care:

PCC (person-centred care) = V+I+P+S

V   *value* base that asserts the absolute value of all human lives regardless of age or cognitive ability

I   *individualised* approach, recognising uniqueness

P   understanding the world from the *perspective* of the service user

S   providing a *social* environment that supports psychological needs

Brooker 2007

PERSON-CENTRED PLANNING

Initially developed for use in learning disability services by writers such as **John O'Brien**, person-centred planning is an active application of person-centred working. **The Department of Health** (2010) refer to person-centred planning as:

▶ A way of discovering what people want, the support they need and how they can get it

▶ Assisting people in leading an independent and inclusive life

▶ A set of tools to promote change

They identify four main approaches to person-centred planning:

1   ELP (Essential Lifestyle Planning)
2   PATH (Planning Alternative Tomorrows with Hope)
3   MAPS (Making Action Plans)
4   Personal Futures Planning

Different services will use different methods of person-centred planning and these will involve the use of different tools and documentation. However, **Sanderson** (2010) asserts that 'for people being supported by services, it is not person-centred planning that matters as much as the pervasive presence of person-centred thinking'. This demonstrates that it is not the process and the tools that are so important – it is more about the values and the way that staff work with service users that communicates person-centred practices.

PERSON-CENTRED TOOLS

A wide range of tools are in use in person-centred planning and in services which take a person-centred approach to working with people. These have been developed mostly from learning disability services and are based on the work of well-known practitioners such as John O'Brien, Beth Mount and Helen Sanderson.

A range of these tools are available on the internet. Some of the most widely used tools are explained on the following pages. However, it is important that care staff make use of the tools utilised in their service and that they have specific knowledge on how these tools should be used with individuals.

One page profile

This is really a one page profile of an individual. Nothing unique in that, you might think! However, it must not focus on needs and disabilities, as many individual user profiles do. Rather, in person-centred thinking, a one page profile lists what people like and admire about the person, what the person feels is important to them and what excellent support for the person would involve.

Good day/bad day

This explores what makes a good day for someone – what they do, where they go, who is there, etc, and what makes a bad day. A good day would be one which the person enjoys and finds meaningful and a bad day would be one where they feel little has been achieved. Learning about what makes a good day and what makes a bad day can help inform planning so that people can have more good days than bad days.

Pyramid of success

This is a way of helping people identify the steps they need to take to work towards their goal. It also identifies who might be able to assist. Where there are difficulties to be overcome on the way to the goal, 'obstacles' can be placed in the way and discussion can take place about how these can be addressed.

Staff matching tools

A range of tools are available to help people identify the characteristics of staff they would like to support them. These are often used when people are considering using personal budgets to employ PAs. Essentially, the idea of this is that service users have control over deciding who supports them.

Lifelines

These are a pictorial way of showing someone's life story – it helps identify where a person is at and how they got there – it can also be developed to show where they want to go to next.

4 + 1 questions

This essentially involves asking four questions:

1   What have we tried?
2   What have we learned?
3   What are we pleased about?
4   What are we concerned about?

and then following this up with the +1 question – so what do we need to do?

Personal communication passports

Developed in the 1990s by Sally Millar, a specialist speech and language therapist at the Communication Aids for Language Centre (**CALL**), these are a practical tool which aim to describe the most effective ways of communicating with an individual.

PREVENTION AND EARLY INTERVENTION

Many sectors now recognise the vital importance of taking a preventative approach to service delivery. For example, the fire service has changed much of its working practice, recognising that preventing deaths from fire is best achieved through practices such as removing/addressing fire risks and providing equipment such as smoke detectors. **Leadbetter** (2008) draws on the fire service approach as a comparison with social care. He claims that social care is 'good at fire engines but needs more smoke detectors'.

The aim of prevention services is to support people by early intervention to prolong good health and quality of life. The active promotion of health, wellbeing and independence (rather than waiting for people to become ill and then treating them) is fundamental to personalisation and should now be a cornerstone of local authority policy. Social care has a vital role to play in keeping people out of hospital, delaying their need for long term care and helping them to stay in their own homes for as long as possible.

Humphries (2006) reported that Government consultations indicate overwhelming public support for preventative services. For example, in the consultation that the Government did around the White Paper *Our Health, Our Care, Our Say* 80% of people supported a shift towards preventative services.

As a result of this, the Government reported four key targets:

▶ Better prevention and early intervention in terms of public health and wellbeing
▶ Giving people more choice and a louder voice
▶ Tackling inequalities
▶ Better support for people with long term conditions.

THE THREE STAGES OF PREVENTION

Primary prevention – the focus is on preventing problems before they happen. For example, by encouraging people to engage with their local communities and so avoid social isolation.

Secondary prevention – this involves working with people who are known to be at risk and intervening with the aim of preventing further deterioration. For example, providing falls prevention support to someone who has already had a fall and is at risk of another fall.

Tertiary prevention – this involves working with someone who already has an ongoing social care need to improve quality of life, and, if possible, to reduce the need, for example, by providing reablement services.

PREVENTION IN THE COMMUNITY

In the broadest sense, prevention services include a wide range of activities within the community that will help to promote health and wellbeing. The following have been identified as particularly important aspects of preventative services:

- *Information and advice*
- *Housing and practical support*
- *Promoting physical activity*
- *Reducing isolation and social exclusion, and broadening social and community networks*
- *Ensuring access to mainstream services*

Peter Fletcher Associates 2010

TELECARE

Telecare refers to a wide range of devices that can be used within the home to monitor and protect people or to make their life easier. These include:

- ▶ Devices that are monitored remotely, such as:
    - ▶ detectors for falls, fire and gas
    - ▶ pendants that detect movement – for example, if the person leaves their home
    - ▶ motion sensors for beds that can detect if a person gets up during the night
- ▶ Fingerprint recognition for door entry systems
- ▶ Systems that remind people to perform daily tasks or to take their medication

PERSONALISATION AND PERSON-CENTRED CARE

DISADVANTAGES OF TELECARE

Telecare can enable people to remain in their own homes for longer and to retain their independence, but it does have some disadvantages:

▶ Some people may find it intrusive and feel that their privacy is being invaded
▶ If good failsafe systems are not in place, the person may be at risk if there is a technical fault
▶ It can increase social isolation because of the reduced need for human contact
▶ It may not be used properly, eg a safety pendant may be removed if the person doesn't like wearing it
▶ Even the most advanced technology may not recognise that a telecare user is at risk or has health problems, even though these might be obvious to a human being

FALLS PREVENTION

Older people are much more likely to fall than younger people and their injuries are much more likely to be serious and take longer to heal or lead to complications. Fractures of the wrist and femur (thigh bone) are particularly common. Effective falls prevention can therefore have a major impact on the health and wellbeing of older people and can potentially keep them out of hospital and even prolong their lives. Even falls that do not cause serious injury can lead to a loss of confidence. However, falls prevention is a challenge to health and social care services. People who are at risk are difficult to monitor, particularly when they are living in their own homes.

The following all contribute to falls prevention:

▶ Promoting exercise activity – helping people to maintain their muscle power, joint strength and balance reduces the likelihood of falls

▶ Ensuring safety – hazards in the home, such as loose rugs on polished floors, can lead to serious injury

▶ Effective management of health problems – a large number of health problems can increase the risk of falls

▶ Effective management and regular review of medication – some medications can increase the risk of falls

▶ Advice on alcohol intake – even small amounts of alcohol can cause falls in older people

PERSONALISATION AND PERSON-CENTRED CARE

REABLEMENT

The aim of reablement (or tertiary) services is to assist people with physical difficulties, learning disabilities or mental health problems to learn or relearn the basic skills necessary for daily living, such as washing, dressing and cooking. The emphasis is on helping people to regain physical abilities that they may have lost because of illness or disability so that they can remain independent and manage their daily lives, despite their health problems and potential limitations.

Those working in reablement take a 'hands-off' approach and encourage service users to do things for themselves (with tailor made support). Services are provided for a limited period, usually 6–12 weeks. Reablement services are also seen as cost-efficient because they can remove, reduce or delay the need for long term care services.

EXTRA CARE HOUSING

Extra care housing provides more support than sheltered housing but enables people to have more independence than they would have in a care home. Easy care schemes are developments of flats (or sometimes bungalows) where round the clock support is provided on site. Larger developments are known as Extra care villages. The accommodation is adapted for the needs of occupants with facilities such as walk in showers. Flats may be rented or bought by individuals or couples. Extra care is suitable for people who may have high support needs – for example, they may not be able to get up without help in the morning – but can otherwise live safely on their own.

SELF-DIRECTED SUPPORT

Self-directed support is about increasing the control that people have over how to spend the money available for their care and support. It involves the calculation of personal or indicative budgets and the provision of direct payments.

Since the **Community Care (Direct Payments) Act** (1996) people who have been assessed as being eligible for social care have had the option to take a cash direct payment to purchase the support they choose, once it has been discussed and negotiated with their care manager.

More recently there has been a move towards individual budgets. While direct payments only use money from a local authority social care budget, individual budgets combine resources from different funding streams to which an individual is entitled, including benefits, etc. There have been a range of difficulties with this approach, so many authorities still use direct payments to facilitate self-directed support.

Individual budgets use a **Resource Allocation System** (RAS) to distribute funds so that an individual knows how much money is available to them. Unlike a direct payment, individual budgets can be operated in several ways:

▶ By the individual as a cash direct payment
▶ By the care manager
▶ By a trust
▶ As an indirect payment to a third party
▶ Held by a service provider

HOW CAN PERSONAL BUDGETS/DIRECT PAYMENTS BE SPENT?

A personal budget can be used for:

► Employing support workers or personal assistants
► Paying expenses for unpaid helpers
► Paying for support to attend college courses unless alternative funding is available
► Supporting attendance at places of worship
► Supporting participation in sport and other leisure activities
► Support voluntary work
► Buying a season ticket for sporting fixtures for a personal assistant or friend so that they can go to matches with the service user
► Buying equipment that will reduce long term support needs or will reduce risks

A personal budget can also be used for one-off activities, such as:

► A holiday with family, friends or support worker as an alternative to respite care at a care home

► A day trip

► Occasional sports events or concerts

► Driving lessons to improve job prospects

A personal budget/direct payment cannot be used for:

► Anything illegal

► Gambling

► Buying food or clothes or paying household bills

► Paying off debts

► Employing family members, unless agreed by the local authority

► Services that should be provided by the NHS

Khayriyah

I used to have meals on wheels. Most days I didn't eat them because there was no halal option. In the review of my support plan I talked to my care manager about how little I liked the meals. She told me about the option of having direct payments. I wasn't keen on it at first, but when I talked it over with my family I decided to give it a try. It's great! A support worker Aysha comes in to help me to prepare the kind of food I like. No more unfinished plates.

PERSON-CENTRED WORKING AND RISK

Risk is an inevitable part of life for everyone. However, very often people who are in contact with social care services are over protected from risks. There is a certain dignity to risk-taking which can be denied to service users.

Approaches which have developed in traditional services which deny the dignity of taking some risks are known as risk averse approaches.

Person-centred approaches recognise the dignity associated with risks and take a positive risk taking approach (sometimes referred to as risk enablement). This involves person-centred risk assessments and individualised approaches to risk management.

DEFINING RISK

Risk is an inevitable part of life and the degree of risk that an individual finds acceptable to take in their life will vary from person to person.

Department of Health 2010

Risk is defined as this uncertainty of outcome, whether positive opportunity or negative threat, of actions and events. The risk has to be assessed in respect of the combination of the likelihood of something happening, and the impact which arises if it does actually happen. Risk management includes identifying and assessing risks (the 'inherent risks') and then responding to them.

HM Treasury 2004

The governing principle behind good approaches to risk is that people have the right to live their lives to the full as long as that does not stop others from doing the same.

Department of Health 2007

WHAT ABOUT HEALTH AND SAFETY AND DUTY OF CARE?

Professionals working from a risk averse approach often quote health and safety or the duty of care when making risk averse plans. However, the:

Health and Safety executive endorses a sensible approach to risk so that health and safety legislation does not prevent reasonable activity.
Department of Health 2010

The duty of care needs to be balanced with 'the duty to involve', which was implemented across England in 2009. It is also important to recognise that case law tends to take a positive and pragmatic approach to risk:

A sensible risk appraisal is not striving to avoid all risk ... (it aims) in particular to achieve the vital good of the ... person's happiness. What good is making someone safer if it merely makes them miserable?
Justice Munby in Department of Health 2010

THE DIGNITY OF RISK

The idea that there is dignity in risk is also sometimes referred to as the 'right to failure'. By taking away all risks from people, they can be denied the right to self-determination – to decide for themselves how they want to live their life, even if the choices they make may not always be the 'best' ones.Empowering people to take risks is not just about allowing or permitting actions to occur. It involves:

▶ Examining your own values in relation to the action the person wants to take
▶ Discussion about the whole range of choices which are available to the person, as well as possible consequences (both positive and negative)
▶ Explaining to others why you are doing this as other people may be challenged by self-determination and risk
▶ Continuing to support the person, even (or maybe especially) if they experience negative consequences as a result of their choice

SAFEGUARDING AND PERSONALISATION

Concerns have been raised that the move towards personalisation may increase the risks that service users face. There are also concerns that service users may not be fully aware of the risks that they face (**Commission for Social Care Inspection** 2008). However, there is increasing research that safeguarding and personalisation can work effectively together.

The Department of Health Consultation on the review of 'No Secrets' (Government Guidance on the safeguarding of vulnerable adults) found that, whilst it was important to find the balance between personalisation and protection, there is evidence that shifting the power balance within families and between service users and professionals can have very positive safeguarding outcomes. It concluded that the Department of Health had a firm belief that personalisation and safeguarding can work together in a complementary way.

PERSONALISATION AS A METHOD OF SAFEGUARDING

A number of supporters of personalisation have challenged professionals, stating that they often begin from the assumption that personalisation automatically increases risk. They counter this by stating that many of the principles of personalisation improve safeguarding and actually decrease risk.

A central theme of personalisation is prevention and early intervention. This is also seen as the key to safeguarding (preventing abuse and exploitation is the aim of safeguarding practice).

Ensuring that people have control over their own lives is a key aspect of personalisation, and in turn this improves safeguarding.

Putting people in control of their own destiny ... strengthens their skills and increases their confidence, facilitating increased connectivity or 'circles of support' which in turn increase the likelihood of potentially abusive situations being noticed. Stronger citizens are much less likely to be the victims of abuse.'
In Control 2009

Traditional overprotective approaches have placed people at increased risk – for example people can be 'placed at risk of being denied a fulfilling life'.
Department of Health 2010

It should not be forgotten that people have been subject to institutional abuse in traditional services – the extent of which is often underplayed by those who oppose personalisation.

Research by **Skills for Care** (2008) identified that people using direct payments to engage personal assistants experienced significantly less abuse than those using traditional council services.

SO WHAT DO I DO?

The Department of Health (2010) offer some practical suggestions for practice that incorporates personalisation and safeguarding. These can be summarised as:

► Develop positive thinking about risk and personalisation
► Never assume risks because of factors such as diagnosis or service use, but base decisions on the individual, their circumstances and their actual statements and behaviours
► Ensure that risk assessment is proportionate to individual circumstances
► Consider the risks involved with people using non-personalised services (loss of confidence, autonomy, etc)

- ▶ Ensure that decisions about capacity are based on the Mental Capacity Act (or other country specific legislation)
- ▶ Look holistically at families and situations
- ▶ Ensure that your practice is reflective
- ▶ Take a holistic approach – liaising with other professionals where appropriate
- ▶ Employ a strengths perspective in your practice and focus on solutions and outcomes
- ▶ Ensure that you are fully conversant with your local safeguarding procedures
- ▶ Encourage people to consider possible risks

PERSON-CENTRED TEAMS

This is a term in regular use in contemporary social care practice. According to **Sanderson** (2011) many teams view person-centred working as creating additional work, rather than as being central to practice. She goes on to say that person-centred planning is not the icing on the cake – it is the cake.

Sanderson (2011) identifies the characteristics of a person-centred team as one which:

- Sees the team's purpose as supporting people to achieve the lifestyle they want and contributing to their community
- Highly values personal commitment and relationships with the people they support
- Sees itself as being with people not over them
- Reviews itself not the people it supports
- Invests in community connections
- Continually tries new ideas and evaluates whether it improves the support it is providing to achieve the team's purpose

WOULD YOUR TEAM BE CONSIDERED PERSON-CENTRED? WHY?

PUTTING IT ALL TOGETHER

The Scottish Government has commented several times that personalisation 'is not rocket science' (eg **Changing Lives Development Group** 2008). However, it is seen as transformational and does require a shift in traditional care practice. Hopefully this Pocket Guide has provided you with some ideas about how to put person-centred care and personalisation into practice, by providing information and practical guidelines. To summarise these, effective person-centred care staff need to:

Recognise that prevention is better than cure: by acting early you can help people to prolong their independence and enjoy a better quality of life.

Remain user-centred at all times: remember that the whole reason you have a job is because of the service user.

Promote dignity and respect in all your work: every individual deserves to be treated with the respect and dignity you would want yourself.

Develop empathic relationships: it is only by putting yourself in someone else's shoes that you can work effectively with them.

Recognise people as unique individuals and respond to them as such: the world would be a very boring place if we were all the same – and services which do not recognise this are outdated and potentially dangerous.

Use a biographical approach: understanding someone's life story can be illuminating and makes for very interesting work.

Recognise strengths: it is important that we focus on what people can do, what they enjoy, etc, rather than on what they need. Starting from a positive perspective creates positive outcomes.

Employ positive person work and effective communication: good relationships begin with good quality communication and this is perhaps the skill most valued by service users.

Recognise and respect the professional value base: social care has a long history and unique positive values; following these will not only ensure better services for those we work with, it will also enhance a worker's job satisfaction.

Take a positive approach to risk: risk is an inevitable part of life but not all risks are worth taking. By providing people with effective person-centred support you can enable people to recognise whether they are safe or not.

Work in partnership: working with service users and their families enables both you and the people you are working with to use our skills to the best effect.

Recognise that collaboration works: developing good relationships with the variety of people who support service users will benefit the people you work with.

A little innovation goes a long way: by thinking creatively you can encourage your team to work in ways which are individually tailored to the needs of the people you support.

Recognise the importance of team work in person-centred care: teams need to develop approaches which are person-centred and everyone in the team has a role to play in this.

REFERENCES

Alzheimer Scotland (2011) *Let's Get Personal: Personalisation and Dementia*. Available online at www.alzscot.org/pages/policy/report-personalisation-and-dementia.htm. Accessed 29.4.11

ARC UK (2011) *Active Support*. Available online at http://arcuk.org.uk/training services/active-support/ Accessed 19.6.11

Avenues (2011) *Person-Centred Active Support*. Available online at http://docs.google.com/viewer?a=v+q=cache:TsaqahTJOHgJ:www.avenuesgroup.org.uk/data/files/active_support_brochure.pdf. Accessed 20.6.11

Brooker, D (2007) *Person-Centred Dementia Care – Making Services Better*. (London) Jessica Kingsley Publishers

Carr, S (2008) *Steps on the Journey: Personalisation – an Introduction*. Available online at http:///docs.google.com/viewer?a=v+q=cache:ydhar2GZUJ Accessed 2.5.11

Carr, S (2010) *SCIE Report 20: Personalisation: A Rough Guide*. (London) SCIE

Community Care in association with Unison (2010) *The State of Personalisation*. Available online at www.communitycare.co.uk/static-pages/articles/the-state-of-personalisation. Accessed 2.11.11

Cunningham, I and Nickson, D (2010) *Personalisation and its Implications for Work and Employment in the Voluntary Sector*. (Glasgow) Scottish Centre for Employment Research

Department of Health (2007) *National Service Framework for Older People*. (London) HMSO

Department of Health (2010) *Practical Approaches to Safeguarding and Personalisation*. (London) Department of Health

Department of Health (2010) *Personalisation through Person-Centred Planning*. (London) Department of Health

Dowling, S, Manthorpe, J, and Cowley, S in association with King, S, Raymond, V, Perez, W and Weinstein, P (2006) *Person-Centred Planning in Social Care: A Scoping Review*. (York) Joseph Rowntree Foundation

Duffy, S and Fulton, K (2010) *Architecture for Personalisation.* (Sheffield) Centre for Welfare Reform

Edwards, T and Waters, J (2008) *It's Your Life – Take Control.* (Hertford) Hertfordshire County Council

Humphries, R (2006) *Our Health, Our Care, Our Say: The Preventative Agenda. Presentation at Older Peoples Wellbeing: Making the Shift Towards Prevention.* ICN Conference London. March 2006

In Control Fact Sheets (2011) Available online at http://www.in-control.org.uk/resources/fact-sheets.aspx. Accessed 10.4.11

Innes, A, Macpherson, S, and McCabe, L (2006) *Promoting Person-Centred Care at the front line.* (York) Joseph Rowntree Foundation

Kerr, L, and Reid, J (2008) *Personalisation Discussion Paper.* (Glasgow) Enable Scotland

Leadbetter (2004) *Personalisation through Participation: A New Script for Public Services.* (London) Demos

Lelkes, J (2010) *Personalisation: A Social Work Perspective.* Available online at www.brighton.ac.uk/sass/research/mrc/resources/personalisation_151210_jackielelkespresentation.pdf. Accessed 20.4.10

National Audit Office (2009) *Supporting Carers to Care.* (London) National Audit Office

Parley, F (2001) 'Person-Centred Outcomes: Are Outcomes Improved where a Person-Centred Care Model is Used?' in *Journal of Learning Disabilities*, vol 5, no 4, pp299–308

Paul Fletcher Associates Ltd (2010) *North East Improvement and Efficiency Partnership. What supports Independence Project. Work Phase 1: Researching the Services that Support Independence. Executive Summary.* Available online at www.northeastiep.gov.uk. Accessed 10.4.11

Rogers, C R (1958) 'The Characteristics of a Helping Relationship' in *Personal and Guidance Journal*, vol 37, pp6–16

Saleeby, D (1996) 'The Strengths Perspective in Social Work Practice: Extensions and Cautions' in *Social Work*, vol 41, pp296–305

Sanderson, H (2003) 'Implementing Person-Centred Planning by Developing Person-Centred Teams' in *Journal of Integrated Care*, vol 11, no 3, pp18–25

Sanderson, H (2010) *What is Person-Centred Thinking and Planning?* Available online at www.helensandersonassociates.co.uk/reading-room/how/person-centred-planning.aspx. Accessed 1.8.11

Sanderson, H (2011) *Person-Centred Teams*. Available online at www.sutton.gov.uk/index.aspx?articleid=2069. Accessed 28.7.11

Simpson, B (2010) *Practical Approaches to Safeguarding and Personalisation.* (London) Department of Health

Social Care Institute for Excellence (2010) *Dignity in Care*. Available online at www.scie.org.uk/publications/guides/guide15/index.asp. Accessed 2.8.11

Social Platform (2010) *Briefing Number 33: Annual Theme 2010 on Care.* (Brussels) Social Platform

The Health Foundation (2011) *Person-Centred Care*. Available online at www.health.org.uk/areas-of-work/topics/person-centred-care/ Accessed 15.6.11

Think Local, Act Personal Partnership (2011) *Think Local, Act Personal.* Available online at www.thinklocalactpersonal.org.uk/library/resources/personalisation. Accessed 10.4.11

Thompson, N (1994) *The Value Base of Health and Social Care.* (Warrington) Prospects Training Publications

Tolan, J (2003) *Skills in Person-Centred Counselling and Psychotherapy.* (London) Sage

Towell, D (2008) *People with Intellectual Disabilities: Exploring Strategies for Achieving Equal Citizenship. Presentation to the International Association for the Scientific Study of Intellectual Disability.* (Cape Town) August 2008

City & Guilds is the UK's leading provider of vocational qualifications, offering over 500 awards across a wide range of industries, and progressing from entry level to the highest levels of professional achievement. With over 8,500 centres in 100 countries, City & Guilds is recognised by employers worldwide.

Publications

For information about, or to order support materials, contact the Publishing department on +44 (0)20 7294 4113 or learningmaterials@cityandguilds.com. More information about the materials is available at www.cityandguilds.com/publications. For further copies of this Pocket Guide, or other qualification documentation, contact our Publication Sales department on +44 (0)20 7294 2850 or by fax +44 (0)20 7294 3387.